The Mensch on a Bench

Written by
Neal Hoffman

Illustrated by
Necdet Yilmaz

Layout by
Rob Foster

Everyone knows the story of the Maccabees and how they led the Jews to freedom....
But... nobody knows about the unsung hero of Hanukkah, Moshe the Mensch. Let me share Moshe's story...

Judah and the Maccabees returned to the temple and celebrated their victory against the Greeks. At the end of the night, when they were ready to go to bed, they realized that they only had enough oil for one night.

(Did you know that the Menorah in the temple had only seven lights and the middle light was not used as the Shamash or the leader?)

A friendly voice replied from the back of the temple, "I will stay up and watch the lights and let you know if it goes out. You and the others get some rest."

Judah said, "Thank you! What is your name, friend?"

The man replied, "My name is Moshe, and I would be happy to sit on this bench and watch over the temple."

"Moshe, you're a Mensch!" Judah said. "A Mensch on a Bench," and the children laughed.

And so the Maccabees, their families, and the rest of the congregation went to sleep. Moshe sat and watched over the light.

To Moshe's amazement, the light stayed lit all night.

In the morning, everyone was amazed that the light was still lit. Surely this little bit of oil could not last two nights.

But sure enough, on the second night, the lights remained lit. And Moshe the Mensch watched over the temple.

On the third day, while the Maccabees went to work, Moshe played with the children. The children were bored and had only clay to play with. They asked Moshe to make up a game for them. So Moshe wrote symbols on the clay, spun it around, and the kids began to play Dreidel.

On the third night, just like the second night, Moshe again watched the lights, and they stayed lit and shone bright.

On the fourth day, the children wanted to thank Moshe for playing with them. So they made special presents for him, wrapped them, and let him open them up in front of them. Oy... how Moshe smiled!

On the fourth night, Moshe the Mensch watched over everyone and the lights remained lit.

On the fifth day the children were tired of eating the same boring food for days in a row and asked Moshe to make them a treat. Moshe made his famous Latkes... filled up everyone's bellies... and made everyone smile. What a Mensch!

On the fifth night, Moshe again watched as the light shone bright on the Jews of the temple. Surely, it could not last six nights!

On the sixth day, the Jewish people of the temple knew that something special was happening. They joined together and celebrated with songs, just like we still do to this day.

On the sixth night, Moshe watched as the lights shone bright, and the Jewish people watched with him as the miracle of G-D shone before them.

On the seventh day, the Sabbath, the Jews rested. Tired from staying up all night, Moshe rested too! The kids watched the lights and made sure they did not go out. The oil continued to burn.

On the seventh night, the miracle of the lights continued... and Moshe the Mensch smiled, as he knew that G-D was watching out for his people.

On the eighth day, the Jews celebrated as the miracle continued. Moshe snuck away, and when nobody was looking, filled everyone's pockets with coins made of candy, called Gelt! Everyone was so happy... what a Mensch!

On the eighth night, after the oil had lasted for eight long days, more oil arrived at the temple! The Jews, now free, celebrated and knew that G-D had sent them a sign. They told their children to always remember this Festival of Lights... and told them to always try to be a Mensch (or a good person).

Today... Jewish families from around the world can celebrate Hanukkah with their own Mensch on a Bench watching over their Menorah!

There are 8 important rules you must follow when you bring a new Mensch into your home.

Rule 1: Name your Mensch! Each Mensch is special and should be part of your family.

Rule 2: Moshe was always trying to make the kids smile and have fun.Enjoy this holiday with your family... have fun... make your own traditions. Put more Funukkah into Hanukkah!

Rule 3: Every day of Hanukkah, make sure you give your Mensch a Shamash candle to hold... and every night use that candle to light your Menorah.

Rule 4: Mensches are infused with Hanukkah magic. Make sure your kids know that if they behave, your Mensch will let go easily of the Shamash candle, but if they misbehave, he will hold it tight, and they may not get any presents.

Rule 5: Your Mensch will get sore from sitting in one place for too long, just like Moshe... so move him every day. Mensches love to have fun.... so be creative with your Mensch.

Rule 6: Mensches love having their pictures taken! Take fun photos and share them online with friends and family each night of Hanukkah.

Rule 7: One night of Hanukkah don't open presents yourself, *instead buy presents and give them to people in need. Remember that a true Mensch is one who puts smiles on other people's faces.*

***Rule 8:** Mensches don't sleep. Let them watch over the Menorah at night.*

A special thanks to the Mensches of Mention who made this all possible. Each of you is a Mensch in your own right!

*The first letter of each word in the phrase Nes, Godol, Hayah, Sham are the letters on the dreidel.
Nun, Gimel, Hay, Shin

BLESSING OVER CANDLES
בָּרוּךְ אַתָּה יְיָ אֱלֹהֵינוּ מֶלֶךְ הָעוֹלָם, אֲשֶׁר קִדְּשָׁנוּ
בְּמִצְוֹתָיו, וְצִוָּנוּ לְהַדְלִיק נֵר שֶׁל חֲנֻכָּה.
Blessed are You, Adonai our God,
Sovereign of all, who hallows us with mitzvot,
commanding us to kindle the Hanukkah lights.
BLESSING FOR HANUKKAH
בָּרוּךְ אַתָּה יְיָ, אֱלֹהֵינוּ מֶלֶךְ הָעוֹלָם, שֶׁעָשָׂה נִסִּים
לַאֲבוֹתֵינוּ בַּיָּמִים הָהֵם בַּזְּמַן הַזֶּה.
Blessed are You, Adonai our God,
Sovereign of all, who performed wonderous
deeds for our ancestors in days of old
at this season.
SHEHECAYANU FIRST NIGHT ONLY
בָּרוּךְ אַתָּה יְיָ אֱלֹהֵינוּ מֶלֶךְ הָעוֹלָם, שֶׁהֶחֱיָנוּ וְקִיְּמָנוּ
וְהִגִּיעָנוּ לַזְּמַן הַזֶּה.
Blessed are You, Adonai our God,
Sovereign of all, for giving us life,
for sustaining us,
and for enabling us to reach this season.

MY HANUKKAH MEMORIES

MY MENSCH BECAME PART OF
OUR FAMILY ON......................OF 20..........
WE NAMED HIM..
BECAUSE...

BEST HANUKKAH MEMORY

20__...
20__...
20__...
20__...
20__...

BIGGEST HANUKKAH SURPRISE

20__...
20__...
20__...
20__...
20__...

FAVOTITE PRESENT

20__...
20__...
20__...
20__...
20__...

MITZVAHS

20__...
20__...
20__...
20__...
20__...